AGES 4–5

# R Mental Maths

## Daily Workout

### Val Mitchell

Pearson Education Limited
Edinburgh Gate
Harlow
Essex, CM20 2JE
England

© Pearson Education Limited 1999

ISBN 0582 41072 X

Designed by Ken Vail Graphic Design, Cambridge.

Printed in China
SWTC/01

The publisher's policy is to use paper manufactured from sustainable forests.

# Introduction

**Mental Maths Daily Workout** is a series of books for pupils aged 4–11.

Book R for pupils aged 4–5 in Reception/P 1.

Book 1 for pupils aged 5–6 in Year 1/P 2.

Book 2 for pupils aged 6–7 in Year 2/P 3.

Book 3 for pupils aged 7–8 in Year 3/P 4.

Book 4 for pupils aged 8–9 in Year 4/P 5.

Book 5 for pupils aged 9–10 in Year 5/P 6.

Book 6 for pupils aged 10–11 in Year 6/P 7.

**Mental Maths Daily Workout** contains two types of mental activities:

■ ORAL maths activities where the questions and responses are verbal. The ORAL maths sections should be used every day at the beginning of the Numeracy Lesson.

■ MENTAL maths copymasters which practice the mental skills that you will be developing with the children in your oral maths session. Instructions and Teaching Tips for the Activity Sheet are given on the non-photocopiable page, beneath the ORAL maths activity.

■ The ORAL maths activities have been designed as whole class activities.

■ Each unit's ORAL activities represent approximately one week's work for approximately 5–10 minutes each day and have a clearly stated purpose.

■ Once you have used a particular activity and once the children are familiar with a particular resource, you can continue using it in subsequent weeks alongside the new activities that are introduced in every unit.

■ There is a guide to the resources you will need for the activities on pages 62–64.

The Mental Maths Record Sheet on page 61 provides teachers with a chart for recording the date a particular unit was completed and any appropriate notes.

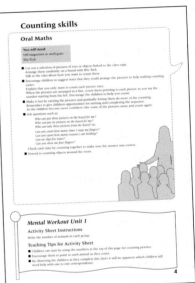

# CONTENTS

# Counting skills

## Oral Maths

**You will need:**
Old magazines or catalogues
Blu-Tack

■ Cut out a selection of pictures of toys or objects linked to the class topic.
Arrange these randomly on a board with Blu-Tack.
Talk to the class about how you want to count these.

■ Encourage children to suggest ways that they could arrange the pictures to help making counting easier.
Explain that you only want to count each picture once.
When the pictures are arranged in a line, count them pointing to each picture as you say the number starting from the left. Encourage the children to help you count.

■ Make it fun by varying the pictures and gradually letting them do more of the counting.
Remember to give children opportunities for starting and completing the sequence.
As the children become more confident take some of the pictures away and count again.

■ Ask questions such as:

*Who can put three pictures on the board for me?*
*Who can put six pictures on the board for me?*
*Who can take three pictures from the board? etc.*

*Can you count how many times I snap my fingers?*
*Can you count how many crayons I am holding?*
*Can we clap five times?*
*Can you show me four fingers?*

Check each time by counting together to make sure the answer was correct.

■ Extend to counting objects around the room.

## *Mental Workout Unit 1*

### Activity Sheet Instructions

Write the number of animals in each group.

### Teaching Tips for Activity Sheet

■ Children can start by using the numbers at the top of this page for counting practice.

■ Encourage them to point to each animal as they count.

■ By observing the children as they complete this sheet it will be apparent which children still need help with one to one correspondence.

\*    \*\*    \*\*\*    \*\*\*\*    \*\*\*\*\*

1     2     3     4     5

# Numbers 1–5

## Oral Maths

### Spider Counting

**You will need:**

A black glove with two 'eyes' stuck to the index finger

Number Cards 1–5 (see the Resource Guide on pages 62–64)

Small cards with pictures of 1–5 bugs/flies arranged as you would find dots on dice

Small cards with pictures of 1–5 bugs/flies arranged in a line

■ Count along the numerals saying the names of the numbers clearly.
Repeat this encouraging the children to join in.

■ Introduce your 'gloved hand' and explain that it is a spider that likes eating bugs.
Choose one of the bug cards and ask the children to help the spider count the bugs.
Ask the children which number card goes with this card.
If they get the correct number turn the card over and pretend the spider has eaten the bugs and is very happy.
Continue until they have completed both the sets of cards. It is helpful for children to see different arrangements of each number of bugs.

■ Ask questions such as:

*How many bugs can the spider eat this time?*
*Which number matches this set of bugs?*
*How many bugs are on this card?*

### Flower Petals

**You will need:**

Six flower centres with stalks, with a number 1–5 written on each centre. (Flowers could be produced by a small group helped by a teaching assistant as an art activity.)

15 flower petals with double sided tape at one end

■ Arrange the stalks on the table or floor.
Point out the numbers written on the centre of each flower.

■ Ask the children to put the correct number of petals on each flower.
These can then be used for a classroom display.

## *Mental Workout Unit 2*

### Activity Sheet Instructions

Give each snowman the number of buttons written in his hat.
Trace over the numbers then draw one of your own.

### Teaching Tips for Activity Sheet

■ Children need to look at the number on each snowman's hat and count the buttons as they draw them.

■ Encourage children to say the number, and draw the buttons, counting as they draw.
They should then trace the appropriate numbers, and finally write their own.

# Sequences

## Oral Maths

### Rhymes and Songs

■ Introduce counting rhymes.
Here are some that you can use.

*One, two, buckle my shoe.*
*Three, four, knock at the door.*
*Five, six, pick up sticks.*
*Seven, eight, lay them straight.*
*Nine, ten, start again.*

*One, two, three, four, five,*
*Once I caught a fish alive.*
*Six, seven, eight, nine, ten,*
*Then I let it go again.*
*Why did you let it go?*
*Because it bit my finger so.*
*Which finger did it bite?*
*This little finger on the right!*

*One, two, three and four,*
*Hippos banging on my door.*
*Five, six, seven and eight,*
*Hippos jumping on my gate.*
*Nine and ten are in their den*
*Munching on my lunch again.*

### Magpie Rhyme

*One for sorrow, two for joy,*
*Three for a girl, four for a boy,*
*Five for silver, six for gold,*
*Seven for a secret never to be told.*

■ Repeat the rhyme and encourage the children to join in.
Use a number line to reinforce the numbers.
Point to each number as it is said.

■ Have fun trying to make up new lines for eight, nine and ten magpies.
For example:

*Eight for sugar, nine for jam,*
*Ten for a great big Suffolk ham.*

## *Mental Workout Unit 3*

### Activity Sheet Instructions

Colour the objects to match the number.

### Teaching Tips for Activity Sheet

■ It can be helpful for children to put a small dot of colour on each picture as they count up to the target number.

■ They can then go back and colour each picture in more detail.

# Unit 3

3

5

1

2

4

# 1–10 numberline

## Oral Maths

### Wash Day

**You will need:**

A Mathematical Washing Line (see the Resource Guide
pages 62–64) with 10 pegs spaced at regular intervals

10 socks labelled 1–10

Number Cards 1–10 (see the Resource Guide pages 62–64)

Picture cards 1–10

- Hand out the socks.
  Ask which sock needs to go at the start of the line.
  Peg the socks up in order.
  Encourage the children to go back and count from 1 after each new sock is added,
  first with and then, as they become more confident, without help.

- Hand out Number Cards 1–10
  Ask children to come up and match their number to the same one on the numberline.

- Vary this activity by pegging different things to the line, e.g.
  hats with numbers pinned to them,
  picture cards 1–10.

- Extend this by making the socks alternate colours for:
  counting in twos
  seeing odd and even number patterns.
  Turn one or more of the socks over so that the numeral cannot be seen.

- Ask questions such as:

  *Which number/numbers are hiding?*

  *Can you find the card that shows the number that is missing?*

  Suggest that two children hide their eyes while two turn over two socks to
  hide the numerals.
  Ask the first pair to find the cards that show the numbers
  that are missing.
  Everyone can check whether they are correct.

## *Mental Workout Unit 4*

### Activity Sheet Instructions

Fill in the missing numbers.

### Teaching Tips for Activity Sheet

- Encourage children to point to the numbers and spaces as they count.
- Point out the number line in the classroom to help those children who need support with the
  shape of some numbers.
- Writing the number in the air with their finger first can help ensure that the correct number is
  recorded and that children are not reversing number shapes.

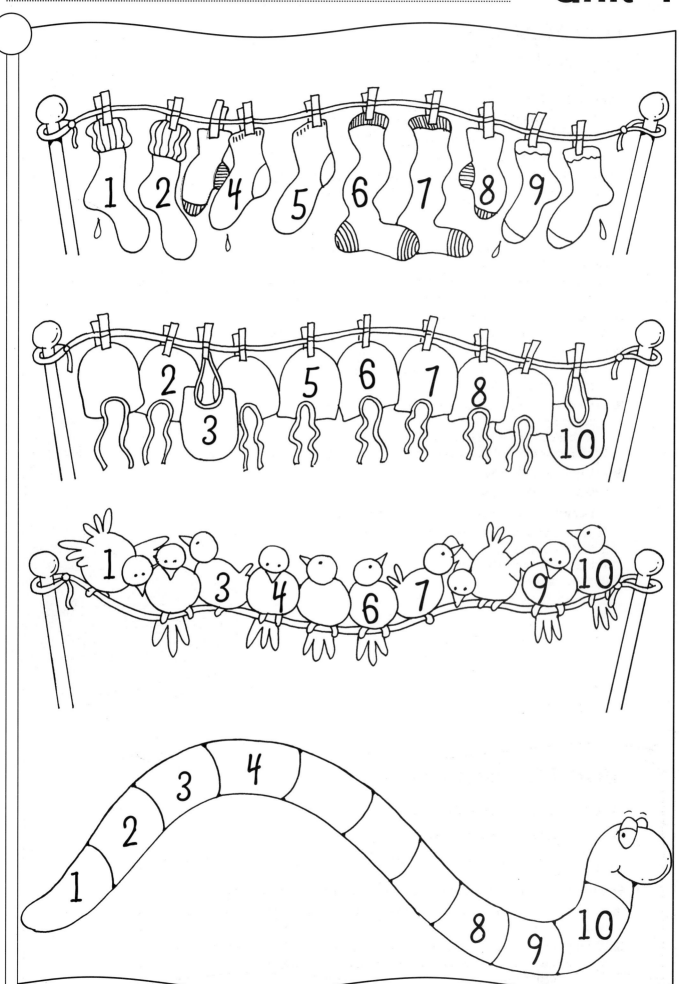

# Finger counting

## Oral Maths

### Hands Up

**You will need:**
A Numberline 1–10 (see the Resource Guide pages 62–64)

■ Start by reminding children how to count on the Numberline.
Explain that we are very lucky we have an easy to use Numberline if we look at our hands.
Start at 1 and count as far as 5. Then repeat showing the children how to use their hand.
Raise each finger as you count, starting with the thumb.
When children are confident extend to 6–10.

■ Point to a number on the Numberline.
Ask the children to show you the same number using their hands.
Encourage the children to check that they are right by counting and pointing to each finger.
Remember to give children opportunities to match the number and count with you to check they are correct.

■ Variations could be:
making a variety of picture cards that represent numbers (monsters with 1–10 spots, planets with 1–10 rockets on, etc.) asking children to hold up the same number of fingers as spots.

### Cars

**You will need:**
A hoop
A selection of 10 toy vehicles

■ Place different numbers of toy cars/buses/vans 0–10 in a hoop.
Ask children to show you how many are in the hoop using their fingers.

■ Encourage children to put up fingers if you put extra cars in and take fingers down if you remove cars.

■ Remember to practise '0 cars'.

## Mental Workout Unit 5

### Activity Sheet Instructions

Draw the correct number of rockets on each planet.
Give the monsters the correct number of spots.

### Teaching Tips for Activity Sheet

■ Ensure that you fill in the number of rockets to be drawn on each planet.
You can vary the numbers so that children are unable to copy from each other.

■ Fill in the number of spots that you want each child to draw on each monster.

# Ordering 1–10

## Oral Maths

### Order and Match

> **You will need:**
> Picture cards of dogs and bones (see the Resource Guide pages 62–64)
> Number cards 1–10 (see the Resource Guide pages 62–64)

- Distribute the picture cards.
  Ask the children to arrange the cards in a line starting with the dog with the least bones.
  Encourage children to check by counting from 1 each time a new card is added.
- Distribute the Number Cards.
  Ask children to match their Number Card with the bones on each picture card and place it under the picture. Ensure that they are matching the number of bones with the correct Number Card. Use this ordered line to help with the next activity.

### Bones

**More Than**

- Introduce the words *'more than'*.
  Explain using the picture cards with 3 bones and 1 bone.
  Hold up the picture of the dog with 3 bones.
  Say: *This dog has* more than *this dog*.
  Hold up the dog with 1 bone.
- Encourage children to come and pick up two cards and show the class which dog has more bones.
  Children can count the bones on each card to check.
  Make sure that the cards are replaced after each turn.
- Extend this by asking children to collect the appropriate number cards when they replace the picture cards.
  Children can then be helped to show that 3 is more than 1 using the number cards.

**Less Than**

- Introduce the words 'less than'.
  Explain using the picture cards with 2 and 5 bones.
  Hold up the picture of the dog with 2 bones.
  Say: *This dog has* less than *this dog*.
  Hold up the dog with 5 bones.
- Repeat the activities used for 'More Than'.

## *Mental Workout Unit 6*

### Activity Sheet Instructions

Fill in the spaces with the correct words or signs. More than (>), Less than (<), Equal to (=).

### Teaching Tips for Activity Sheet

- Encourage the children to talk about what the pictures show.
  Has the first cat got more than the second cat?
  Has the second cat got more fish?
  Has the first cat got more fish?
  Have both cats got equal numbers of fish?

# Unit 6

More than

Less than

Equal to

>      <      =

①    ②    ③    ④    ⑤

# Numbers 11–20

## Oral Maths

### Buckle My Shoe

*Eleven, twelve, dig and delve.*
*Thirteen, fourteen, maids a' courting.*
*Fifteen, sixteen, maids in the kitchen.*
*Seventeen, eighteen, maids in waiting.*
*Nineteen, twenty,*
*My plate's empty!*

**You will need:**

A Numberline 1–20 or the first two lines of an Addition Square (see the Resource Guide pages 62–64)

■ Follow on from 'One, two, buckle my shoe' (page 8).
Start with the part that the children already know and say the rhyme together.
Use the Numberline or the first two lines of an Addition Square to point to the new numbers as you say them.

■ Extend this by progressively replacing the number words with claps or finger taps as you say the rhyme.
First time through,

**Clap**, *twelve, dig and delve* (repeat to the end).

Second time through,

**Clap, clap**, *dig and delve,*

Third time through,

**Clap, clap**, *dig and delve.*

**Snap**, *fourteen, maids a'courting* (etc.)

### Teen Trouble

**You will need:**

Number Cards 1–20 (see the Resource Guide pages 62–64)

Working together

■ Hand out the Number Cards so that they are randomly distributed.
Call out the numbers five at a time, starting with 1–5, followed by 6–10, 11–15 and lastly 16–20.
As you call each set of numbers the children with the matching Number Cards come out and make a Numberline.

■ As children become more confident, extend the activity.
Explain that the teen numbers are always arguing and getting muddled up.
Call the numbers out in different orders, e.g. 12, 14, 15, 11, 13,
Ask the children to get the numbers out of trouble by sorting them into order.

**Extension**

■ Sort numbers in ascending and descending order.

■ Sort larger groups of numbers 1–12, 11–20.

■ Call out a group of numbers with a missing middle number.
Ask children:
*Who has the missing number?*

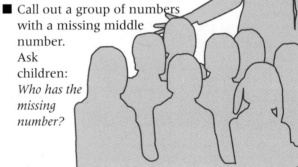

## *Mental Workout Unit 7*

### Activity Sheet Instructions

Fill in the missing numbers.

### Teaching Tips for Activity Sheet

■ Encourage children to count out loud as they point to the numbers on the snakes or ladders. This will give opportunities for assessing whether the children can adapt their counting when the numbers are arranged in order other than left to right orientation.

# Numbers to 100

## Oral Maths

### Stand Up, Sit Down

- Write the numbers 1–50 on the board or use the top half of an Addition Square.
  (see the Resource Guide pages 62–64)
  Encourage the children to join in as you count through from 1 to 50.
  Point to each number on the board as you say it.

- Now count through again but when you say 10, 20, 30, 40, 50, choose an action for the class to do. It could be just putting their hands on their hips or, for the energetic, standing up, turning around and sitting down again.

**Extension**

- Add a different action in for numbers 5, 15, 25, 35, 45:
    - 5 kneel up, sit down
    - 10 stand up, turn around, sit down, etc.

- Extend the game to reach 100.

- Start at different numbers between 1 and 100.

- Try different actions, e.g. thumbs up for numbers ending in 3.

- Sit in a ring and encourage children to count around the ring to 100 so only the children saying numbers 5, 10, 15, 20, etc. do the actions.

### Ants

*There were ten, twenty, thirty ants climbing up the wall,*
*Forty, fifty, sixty ants trying not to fall,*
*Seventy, eighty, ninety ants marching in the hall.*
*I wanted to count a hundred ants,*
*But now there are none at all.*

*There were ten, twenty, thirty ants climbing to the top,*
*Forty, fifty, sixty ants trying not to drop,*
*Seventy, eighty, ninety ants – will they ever stop?*
*I wanted to count a hundred ants,*
*But they're underneath the mop.*

Enjoy making up some more verses!

> **You will need:**
> Decade Cards (see the Resource Guide pages 62–64)

- Hand out the number cards.
  Say the rhyme together.
  Encourage the children holding the appropriate card to stand up when their number is said.

- Ask the children to think up an action to go with the words at the end of each verse.

## *Mental Workout Unit 8*

### Activity Sheet Instructions

Circle the tens and write the correct numbers in the boxes.

### Teaching Tips for Activity Sheet

- Show children how to use this activity page to practise counting in tens.
  Return and start at ten for each new line.
  Line 1: 10    Line 2: 10, 20    Line 3: 10, 20, 30    Line 4: 10, 20, 30, 40
  This will help the children find the answer for the box at the end of each line.

# Unit 8

# Twos and tens

## Oral Maths

### Twos

> **You will need:**
>
> Number Cards 1–20 (see the Resource Guide pages 62–64)

- Sit in a ring and hand out the Number Cards in order. Count round the ring 1–20.
- Now count round again and ask children with even cards to stand up.
  When you reach 20 the children holding 2, 4, 6, 8, etc. will be standing.
  Count these even numbers in order.
  As you say each number the child holding that number sits down.
- The cards can then be passed clockwise one or two places and you can practise again.

### Extension

- Choose an activity for the children holding the odd numbers to do (e.g. kneel).
- Play without using cards.
- Hand out the cards and ask 2, 4, 6, 8, 10 to find each other and 1, 3, 5, 7, 9 to find each other.

### Flower Vase

> **You will need:**
>
> 10 large flowers made from card with a stick and a circular card centre, each
> having 10 petals (You can reuse the flowers made for the activity on page 6
> replacing the numbered centres with plain centres.)
>
> Two sets of Decade Cards (see the Resource Guide pages 62–64)
>
> A vase or container which holds up to 10 flowers without falling over

- Hand out the Decade Cards. Place two flowers in the vase.
  Ask the children to bring out their card if they think their card matches the number
  of petals (20).
- Repeat the activity with different numbers of flowers.
  Remember to give the children opportunities to check by
  counting the flowers (10s) and counting the petals (1s ).
- Children can come out and choose the correct number of
  flowers to match their number card and put them in the vase.
- Children can hold up lots of 10 fingers to show how many
  petals there are.

## *Mental Workout Unit 9*

### Activity Sheet Instructions

Find the numbers in the 2 family and join them together in order.
Colour in all the shapes with a number in the 2 family to see the picture

### Teaching Tips for Activity Sheet

- Show children how to point to the 2 trail before they follow it with a pencil.

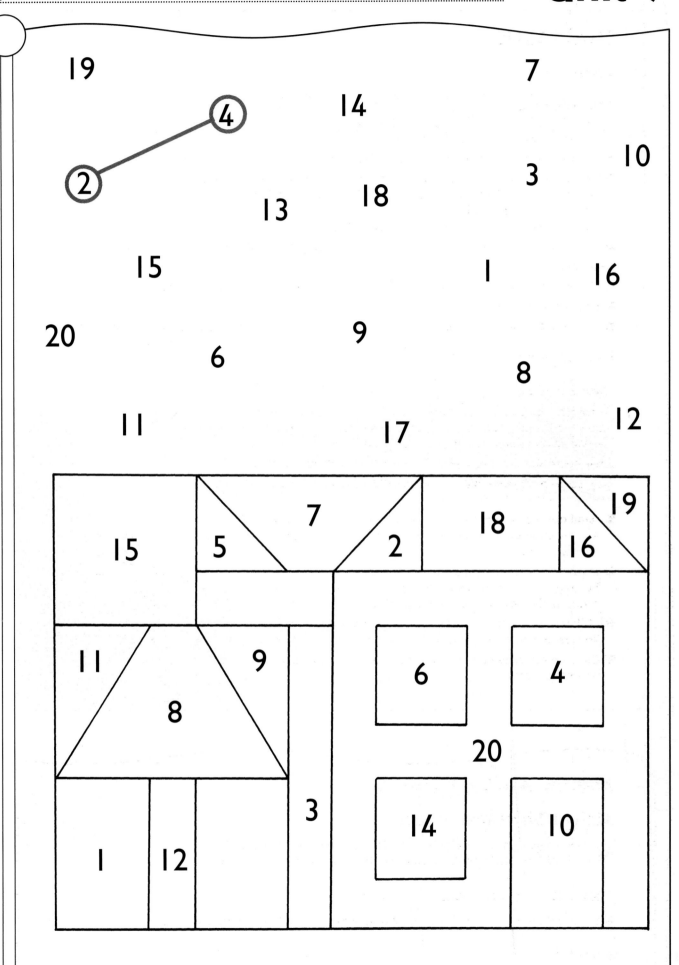

# Ordering 1–20

## Oral Maths
### Ordering

> **You will need:**
>
> Number Cards 1–20 (see the Resource Guide pages 62–64)
>
> Mathematical Washing Line (see the Resource Guide pages 62–64) with 21 pegs at equal intervals (0 is already pegged on the first peg on the left-hand side)

- Hand out the Number Cards
- First count the pegs starting at the first free peg on the left-hand side of the Mathematical Washing Line.
- Count to 20.
- When children are confident start at 1 and ask the children to come and peg their numbers on to the line as you say them.

### Extension

- Start at 20 and work back to 1
- Call the numbers out randomly and ask the children to find where to peg their number by counting the pegs.

> **You will need:**
>
> A glove puppet
>
> Number Cards 1–20 (see the Resource Guide pages 62–64)
>
> Picture cards 1–20
>
> Numberline 1–20 (see the Resource Guide pages 62–64)

### The Card Monster

- Introduce the card monster (your glove puppet). Explain that he isn't very good at reading numbers, so he keeps swapping some of the Number Cards for picture cards.
- Hand out a mixture of Number Cards and Picture cards representing the numbers 1–20. Ask the children to help you sort them on to the Numberline.
- When the line is complete there will be some picture cards left. Explain that each of these needs to be exchanged for the correct Number Card. Ask children to come out and choose the right card from those that the puppet is holding. The children can pretend to be teaching the puppet these numbers.

## *Mental Workout Unit 10*

### Activity Sheet Instructions

Join the dots to find the pictures.

### Teaching Tips for Activity Sheet

- Encourage children to say the numbers as they join them.
- More able children can try starting at 20 and join the dots in reverse order.

Name

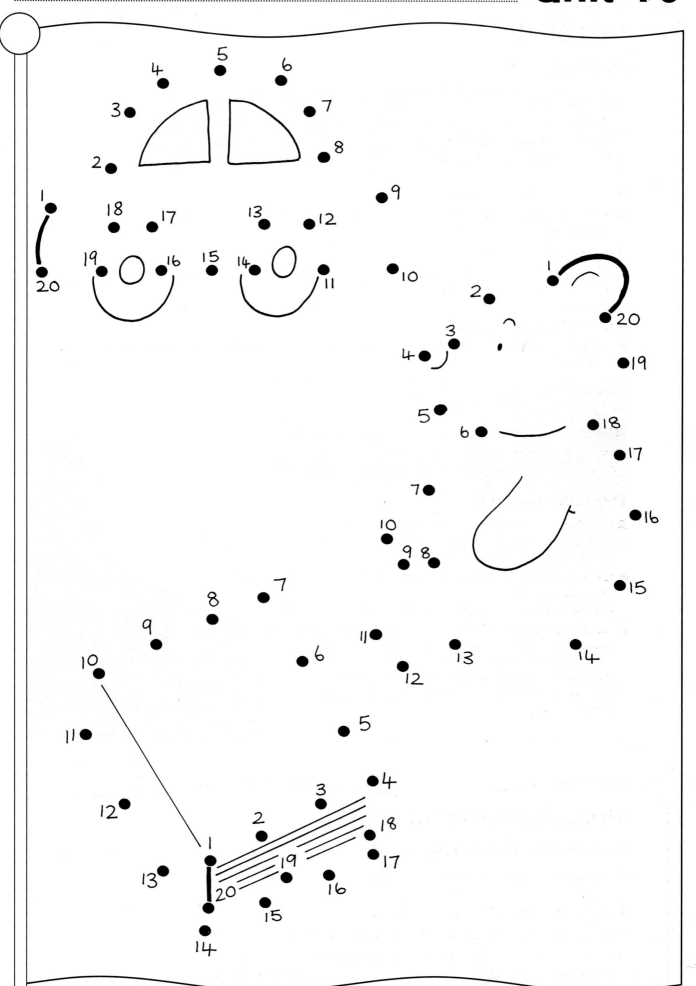

# More or less

## Oral work

### More or Less Than

**You will need:**

Two toys (e.g. a teddy and a doll)

A box (or envelope) for each toy

Number Cards 1–20 (see the Resource Guide pages 62–64)

Picture cards 1–20

A Numberline (see the Resource Guide pages 62–64) 1–20

A red ribbon

■ Explain that teddy collects numbers that are 12 or more and that the doll collects numbers that are less than 12.
Hand out either picture cards or Number Cards.
Ask each child to bring their card out.
Ask: *Is your number more or less than 12?*
When they have decided ask the rest of the class if they agree.
Then place the card in the appropriate box.

■ When all the cards have been placed in the boxes, you can check that each toy is happy with the cards in their box or envelope by matching the card to the Numberline which has a red ribbon tied between the 11 and 12. If the number is to the left of the ribbon it is less than 12 and if it is to the right it is the same as or more than 12.

■ To extend the activity vary the toys and the sorts of numbers that the children collect.
Ask: *Who do you think has more cards in their box?*
Check their answer by counting the cards in each box.

### Post Boxes

**You will need:**

Three boxes with letter box openings, labelled **A** 1–7, **B** 8–14, **C** 15–21

Number Cards 2–6, 9–14, 16–20 (see the Resource Guide pages 62–64)

■ Hand out the cards.
Ask children to think which box their number should be posted in.

■ As children bring their numbers out, ask questions which will help them make their decisions:

*Is your number more than 1?*
*Is your number more than 8?*
*Is your number more than 15?*
*Is your number less than 21?*

Alternatively:

*Is your number less than 21?*
*Is your number less than 14?*
*Is your number more than 8?*

By leaving out the numbers on the boxes you will not have to make decisions about 'the same as'.

## *Mental Workout Unit 11*

### Activity Sheet Instructions

Join the numbers to the toys.

### Teaching Tips for Activity Sheet

■ Show children how to use the Numberline at the top of the page to help them find the answers.

1 2 3 4 5 6 7 8 9 10 11 12 13 14 15 16 17 18 19 20

1

9

12

20

7

13

8

6

3

15

5

10

2

11

14

18

4

16

17

19

Collect numbers more than 12

Collect numbers less than 12

# Estimating

## Oral Maths

### Guess How Many?

> **You will need:**
>
> A selection of boxes with *Multilink* or shells, pasta shapes, conkers, etc.
>
> Make sure that the children cannot hold more of each of these than they can count.
> (Counters for example might be too small.)

- Ask individual children to come out and grab a handful of *Multilink*.
  Explain that they are not going to count each piece but they are going to guess *about how many* they have picked up.
  Ask questions to help model words like **more than**, **less than**, **exactly**, **about**:
    *Do you think you have more than 2?*
    *Do you think you have less than 20?*
    *Do you think you know exactly how many you have?*
    *Can you say about how many you have?*
- Give children opportunities to check how many they are holding by counting in ones or twos, individually or with the class.
- As children become confident with *Multilink* try other things such as *Diennes* blocks (units) or small shells or pieces of pasta.

### Crash!

> **You will need:**
>
> A selection of bricks or boxes to build towers

- Explain that they are going to guess how many bricks or boxes they can stack before the tower falls down. If they put a brick down and the tower falls the last brick doesn't count.
- Show them how to record:

  | My guess/estimate _____ |
  | (choose either word) |
  | My tower _____ |

- Talk about whether their guess was **more than**, **less than**, **exactly the same as** or **about the same as** the number of bricks they actually used.

## *Mental Workout Unit 12*

### Activity Sheet Instructions

Write your estimates in the table. Then count and fill in the exact numbers.

### Teaching Tips for Activity Sheet

Explain that it is important that they make a guess first and that being exactly right does not matter for their first answer. After children have estimated how many windows there might be, it can be helpful for them to use a coloured pencil to mark each window with a dot as they count. Make sure that they use different coloured pencils for the windows, children balls and hoops.

| | My estimate | How many I counted |
|---|---|---|
| Windows | | |
| Children | | |
| Balls | | |
| Hoops | | |

# What comes next?

## Oral maths

### Stepping Stones

**You will need:**

A frog puppet or a cut-out picture of a frog
Large number cards 0–10

- Introduce your frog. Lay out a numberline with 0–10 number cards on the floor. Explain that the frog likes to jump from the smallest numbers up to the biggest, in order. Start by letting him jump up the numberline 0–10 one number at a time. This means that he never gets to do any big jumps.

- Show that if you take some of the numbers away it is much more fun.
  Take off 2, 3, 5, 6, 7, 9.
  Help the frog to jump along the line. Start on 0 and land on 1, 4, 8, 10.

- Ask the children if they can make some new jumping patterns for the frog.

- Choose four children to come out, and give them four cards: 2, 5, 8, 10.
  Hand these out randomly and ask the children to get into a line starting with the smallest number.
  Encourage the rest of the class to help. Check the order with the class using the class numberline. Choose a child to jump the frog along the line of numbers.

**Extension**

- Use numbers 0–20.

- Introduce different coloured frogs that only jump in 2s or 5s.

### Jumping Jacks

**You will need:**

A numberline 0–10 big enough for children to stand on (this could be drawn on the playground with chalk)
Number Cards 1–10 (see the Resource Guide pages 62–64)

Sort the number cards into three piles, (a) 1–3, (b) 4–7, (c) 8–10. Shuffle each pile. Invite a child to take one card from each pile and then choose one more from any pile.

Sort these into order, starting with the smallest. Then each child can jump or step on their numbers along the numberline.

Start by standing on 0.

For example;

       **0** 1 **2** 3 4 5 **6** 7 8 **9** 10

Some may pick hard numbers to jump, e.g. 4–10. This doesn't matter, just say that they will have to fly so they must flap their arms as they walk to this number.

## Mental Workout Unit 13

### Activity Sheet Instructions

Look carefully at the eels and fill in the missing numbers not covered by the jellyfish.

### Teaching Tips for Activity Sheet

- Children should be encouraged to point to each section as they count along the eels to find the missing numbers. This gives opportunities for the class teacher to observe and assess one to one correspondance.

# Unit 13

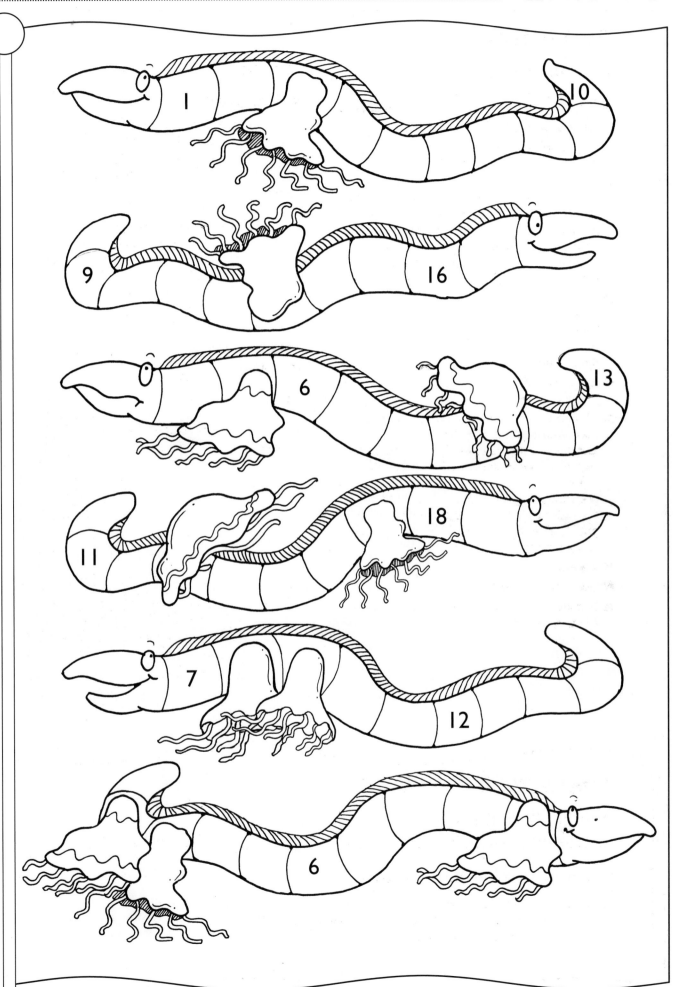

# Making five

## Oral Maths

### Give Me Five

**You will need:**

Some red sticky spots

■ Using your hand show children five fingers and explain that 5 + 0 = 5. Record this on a chart.
Now put a red spot on one finger/thumb.

| No spots | Red spots |
|----------|-----------|
| 5        | 0         |
|          |           |

Show children that there are now four fingers without spots and one with, so that 4 + 1 = 5 as we can still see five fingers.
Record this on the chart.
Now put a red spot on a second finger so there are now three fingers spot free and two fingers with spots.
Ask: *Can you work out this sum?*
Continue until all your fingers have spots on and the children can see that 0 + 5 = 5.

■ Extend the activity by making 'alien' hands that have different numbers of fingers.
Children can then work out ways to make 6, 7, 8, etc. by using different coloured spots.

### Up The Stairs

**You will need:**

Red and blue *Multilink*

■ Show children how to build a tower of 5 *Multilink*.
Give out sets consisting of 1, 2, 3, 4, 5, **red** *Multilink*.
Have a box of **blue** *Multilink* ready.
Ask each child to come out with their red *Multilink* set and, using the blue *Multilink*, make a tower of 5.
As they finish their towers arrange these so that the *Multilink* towers are next to each other and the red *Multilink* makes steps up.
When they are all finished walk your fingers up the red steps to the top of the towers.
Record the sums that these steps make.

■ Extend this by asking children to make towers of 6, 7, 8, etc. They can then record their step sums.

## *Mental Workout Unit 14*

### Activity Sheet Instructions

Record the sums. (The first one is already filled in.)

### Teaching Tips for Activity Sheet

Encourage children to talk about how they are working out the answer. If they are going back and counting all the shapes again to find the answer, show the most confident how to start at the first number and count on. For example, 2 + 3 = 5: say 2, then count 3, 4, 5 to find the answer.

Name

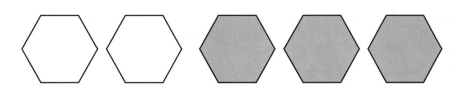

$$\underline{\quad 2 \quad} \ + \ \underline{\quad 3 \quad} \ = \ \underline{\quad 5 \quad}$$

 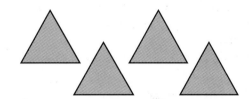

$$\underline{\qquad} \ + \ \underline{\qquad} \ = \ \underline{\qquad}$$

$$\underline{\qquad} \ + \ \underline{\qquad} \ = \ \underline{\qquad}$$

$$\underline{\qquad} \ + \ \underline{\qquad} \ = \ \underline{\qquad}$$

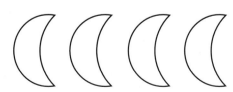 

$$\underline{\qquad} \ + \ \underline{\qquad} \ = \ \underline{\qquad}$$

# Simple addition

## Oral Maths

### Find a Partner

**You will need:**
Picture cards 0–10

■ Hand out a picture card to each child.
Ask children to come out in pairs.
Look at the pictures on each card together.
Count the individual pictures on the left-hand card. Then encourage children to count on from the left-hand card number to find the total of the two cards.

### Fishing Game

**You will need:**

20 fish shapes (These can be made by the children for an art activity prior to the lesson.) Label the fish 0–5: three each of 0, 3, 4 and 5, and four each of 1 and 2.

20 paper clips, one on the mouth of each fish

A large box ('tank') to hold the fish

Fishing rods, each made from a stick with a piece of string which has a small magnet attached at the end

■ Children take turns to come and catch two fish.
They then use the numbers to make an addition sum.
The prizewinning fisherman is the child who makes the largest number with two fish.
■ To extend this the fishermen can be allowed to catch three fish and make a three-number sum.

### Birthday Pairs

**You will need:**

A collection of children's birthday cards with numbers written on to represent ages

A box to put the cards in

■ Ask children to pick out two cards and add the ages together.
Record the sums made.

## *Mental Workout Unit 15*

### Activity Sheet Instructions

Add the numbers on the pairs of fish together to find each fisherman's final score.
Join the cup to the person with the highest score.

### Teaching Tips for Activity Sheet

■ Give children opportunities to tell each other how old they are or when their birthday is.

# Counting On

## Oral Maths

### Hands down

> **You will need:**
> Number Cards 1–8 (see the Resource Guide pages 62–64)

- Hand out the Number Cards 1–8.
  Explain how to count on 3.
  Draw three dots or shapes for the children to count, and write sums
  like this under the dots: __ + 3 =
  Take the '5' number card.
  Write 5 in the first space: _5_ + 3 =
  Put the card down at the front. Put your hand on the card and say 'five'.
  Then point to the dots and count on 3: 'six, seven, eight'.
  Fill in the answer on the board: 5 + 3 = 8.
- Ask children to come out with their cards.
  Encourage them to put their hand on their card, say the number on their card,
  then count on 3 to find the answer.
  Record the sums on the board.
- Extend this by increasing the range of the number cards that the children are
  holding and varying the numbers that you add on.

### 'Add On' Trees

> **You will need:**
> A cardboard display tree or a tree drawn on the board
> Removable labels (e.g. '+ 6') to stick on the tree trunk
> Leaves labelled with single-digit numbers

- Stick a removable label with '+ 6' onto the tree trunk and explain
  that today this is an 'add 6' tree.
  Ask the children to make the sums for this tree.
  These can be written together.
  Encourage the children to pick a leaf, say the number on the
  leaf, then use their fingers to count on 6.
- Extend this by changing the label on the trunk so that
  different numbers can be added.
- For further practise add new leaves with higher numbers.

## *Mental Workout Unit 16*

### Activity Sheet Instructions

Fill in the sums for each tree.

### Teaching Tips for Activity Sheet

Have *Multilink* or coloured counters available for children to check that their sums are correct.

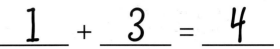

$$\underline{\phantom{1}1\phantom{1}} + \underline{\phantom{3}3\phantom{3}} = \underline{\phantom{4}4\phantom{4}}$$

$$\underline{\phantom{xx}} + \underline{\phantom{xx}} = \underline{\phantom{xx}}$$

$$\underline{\phantom{xx}} + \underline{\phantom{xx}} = \underline{\phantom{xx}}$$

$$\underline{\phantom{xx}} + \underline{\phantom{xx}} = \underline{\phantom{xx}}$$

$$\underline{\phantom{xx}} + \underline{\phantom{xx}} = \underline{\phantom{xx}}$$

$$\underline{\phantom{xx}} + \underline{\phantom{xx}} = \underline{\phantom{xx}}$$

$$\underline{\phantom{xx}} + \underline{\phantom{xx}} = \underline{\phantom{xx}}$$

+3

$$\underline{\phantom{xx}} + \underline{\phantom{xx}} = \underline{\phantom{xx}}$$

$$\underline{\phantom{xx}} + \underline{\phantom{xx}} = \underline{\phantom{xx}}$$

$$\underline{\phantom{xx}} + \underline{\phantom{xx}} = \underline{\phantom{xx}}$$

$$\underline{\phantom{xx}} + \underline{\phantom{xx}} = \underline{\phantom{xx}}$$

$$\underline{\phantom{xx}} + \underline{\phantom{xx}} = \underline{\phantom{xx}}$$

$$\underline{\phantom{xx}} + \underline{\phantom{xx}} = \underline{\phantom{xx}}$$

+5

# Number Bonds

## Oral Maths

### Rhyme

*5 and 5 add up to 10.*
*4 and 6 make it again.*
*3 and 7 will also do.*
*Look carefully, so do 8 and 2,*
*1 and 9 and 0 and 10.*
*Complete the ways of making 10.*

**You will need:**

Red and blue *Multilink*

- Say the rhyme through together.
  Build number bond strips with *Multilink*
  (1 red, 9 blue etc.).
  Ask the children to hold up the number strip
  which matches each line of the rhyme, as you
  say it.

### Picture Pairs

**You will need:**

Two or three sets of picture
cards 0–10

- Call individual children out and show the class
  the card that they are holding.
  Ask if anyone has a card which can be added
  to this card to make 10.
  Continue round the class until everyone is in
  pairs with two cards that make 10.
  Ask all those children who have got 7 and 3 to
  bring their cards out.
  Check that the children understand that it
  doesn't matter which order the cards are in.
  $7 + 3 = 10$    $3 + 7 = 10$

### Toy Tens

**You will need:**

A red hoop and a blue hoop

10 small toys (These could be teddies that
the children have brought from home.)

- Place the hoops on the ground and put all the
  toys in the red hoop.
  Record on the board 10 (red felt pen) add 0
  (blue felt pen) equals 10.
  $10 + 0 = 10$

- Ask if anyone can see another way of
  making 10.
  Encourage any volunteer to move just one toy
  from the red hoop to the blue hoop.
  Record the sum again using the appropriate
  colour pens.
  Keep going until you have moved all the toys
  into the blue hoop.

- For reinforcement use other themes,
  such as:
  10 animals in two pens
  10 cars moving from a garage to a
  car park.

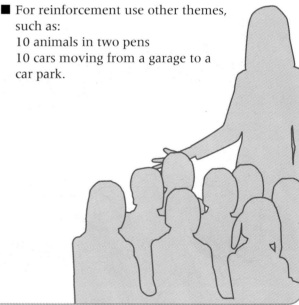

## *Mental Workout Unit 17*

### Activity Sheet Instructions

Fill in the sums.

### Teaching Tips for Activity Sheet

- It can be helpful to have real 10 bead strings for children to use.

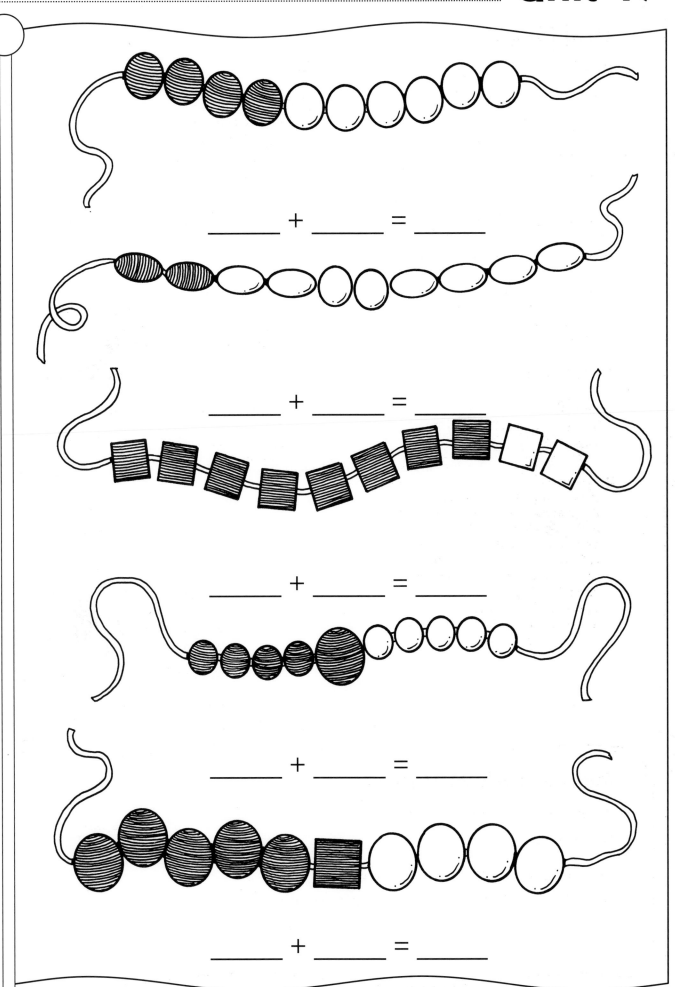

_____ + _____ = _____

_____ + _____ = _____

_____ + _____ = _____

_____ + _____ = _____

_____ + _____ = _____

# Solving problems

## Oral Maths

### Skittles

> **You will need:**
> A set of six skittles labelled 1, 1, 1, 2, 2, 3
> A ball
> A Mathematical Washing Line 0–10 (see the Resource Guide pages 62–64)

■ Set out the skittles, then ask individual children to come out and roll the ball at the skittles.
Collect the skittles that are knocked over.
Together with the children count up the numbers using the Mathematical Washing Line.
As they count each skittle they can stand it back with the others.

### Hungry Toad

■ Tell the children the story of the hungry toad who was always looking for something to eat.
Explain that every day he visited the garden in the morning and the pond in the afternoon.
On Monday he ate 5 flies in the garden and 2 bugs at the pond.
*How many insects did he eat altogether?*
On Tuesday he ate 4 ants in the garden and 3 beetles at the pond.
*How many insects did he eat altogether?*
On Wednesday he ate 6 grasshoppers in the garden and 1 dragonfly at the pond.
*How many insects did he eat altogether?*
On Thursday he ate 3 spiders in the garden and 2 water boatmen at the pond.
*How many insects did he eat altogether?*
On Friday he ate 2 worms in the garden and 4 snails at the pond.
*How many creatures did he eat altogether?*
On Saturday he didn't catch anything at all and he was very hungry!!

Ask the children to think about how many things he ate on Sunday.

## Mental Workout Unit 18

### Activity Sheet Instructions

Fill in the sums.

### Teaching Tips for Activity Sheet

Ask children to explain what they are doing as they work. By observing the children teachers will be able to see whether they are able to count on from the first number or whether they need to start from 1 every time.

Name

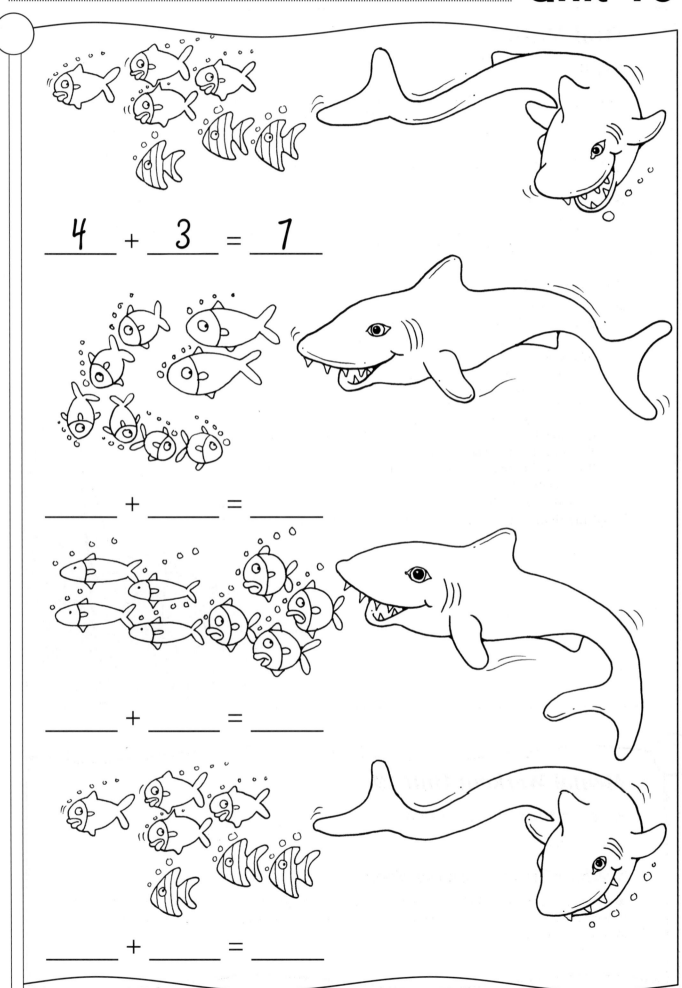

____4____ + ____3____ = ____7____

____ + ____ = ____

____ + ____ = ____

____ + ____ = ____

# Partioning

## Oral Maths

### Rhymes

Counting back rhymes

*Ten green bottles hanging on the wall,*
*Ten green bottles hanging on the wall,*
*And if one green bottle should accidentally fall,*
*There'll be nine green bottles hanging on the wall.*

*Ten little men in a flying saucer,*
*Flew round the world one day.*
*They looked left and right but they didn't like the sight,*
*So one man flew away.*

*Nine little men in a flying saucer …*

Say these rhymes together.
Encourage the children to use their fingers to represent each number.

### Traffic Jams

> **You will need:**
> A selection of toy vehicles
> A dice marked with 1s, 2s and 3s

- Place 10 vehicles in a row to represent traffic waiting at some traffic lights.
  Throw the dice to show how many cars get through each time.
  After each throw record the sum on the board:
  First throw 3
    record 10 – 3 = 7
  Next throw 2
    record 7 – 2 = 5
  Next throw 1
    record 5 – 1 = 4 etc.
- To extend this start with more objects and use an ordinary dice
  for subtraction.
- For reinforcement other themes might be:
  children getting off a bus, (the dice could be marked with
  even numbers only)
  a spider eating flies
  a puppet eating sweets.

## *Mental Workout Unit 19*

### Activity Sheet Instructions

Partition the groups to match the sums.

### Teaching Tips for Activity Sheet

- Encourage the children to draw an imaginary line to partition the sets before
  they draw with a pencil.
- If they have difficulty doing this use a short piece of string to help.

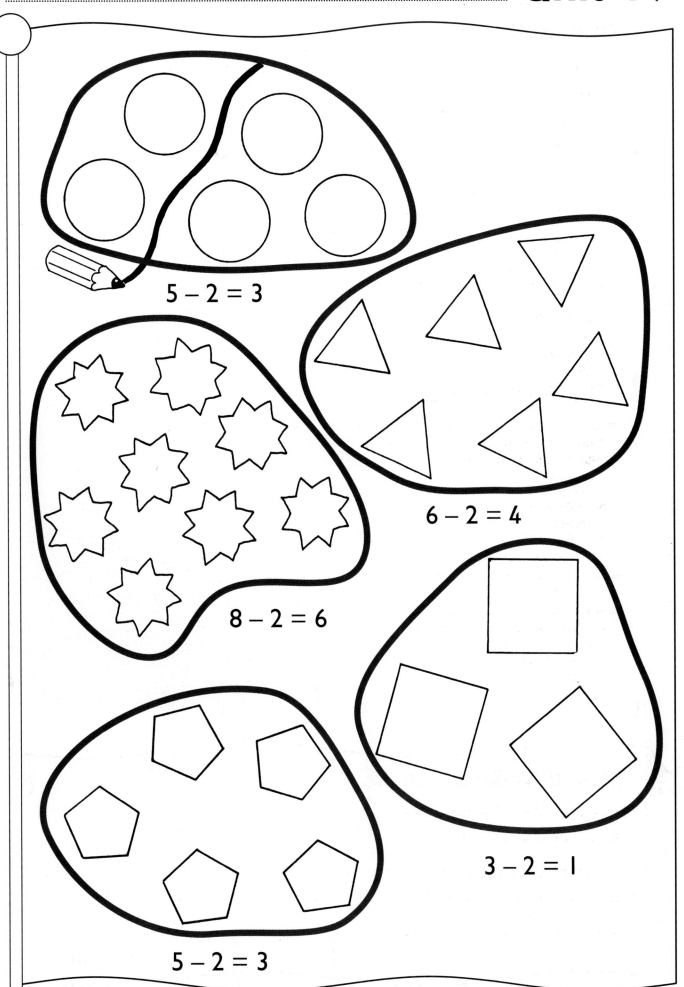

5 − 2 = 3

6 − 2 = 4

8 − 2 = 6

3 − 2 = 1

5 − 2 = 3

# Counting back 10–0

## Oral Maths

### Giant's Footsteps

> **You will need:**
> A numberline 0–10, big enough for children to stand on (This could be drawn on the playground, or made from a roll of wallpaper.).

- Explain that the numberline could continue beyond 10.
  Ask individual children to step back along the line, one number at a time, starting at 10.
  (Make sure that the children take the correct sized steps.)
  Allow everyone to help with the counting.

- Now ask one child to stand on 10.
  Write the sum: $10 - 1 =$
  Ask: *How could we work this out using the numberline?*
  After each sum return to the number 10 on the line and try another sum.
  Write the sum: $10 - 2 =$
  Ask: *How many steps do we need to go back this time?*
  Say with the class:
  *Ten, one step back 9, two steps back 8.*
  Continue to count back from 10.
  $10 - 3 =$    $10 - 4 =$    $10 - 5 =$

- As children become confident ask them to start on a different number and step back,
  e.g. Begin at 6 step back 4, Begin at 9 step back 3, Begin at 5 step back 4.

- To extend this place two children on different numbers on the line and choose a
  lower target number for them to reach.
  Ask: *How many steps will you need to take to get to the target number 2?*
  Encourage children to guess and then check.
  Record these as sums.

## *Mental Workout Unit 20*

### Activity Sheet Instructions

Fill in how many steps.

### Teaching Tips for Activity Sheet

Encourage children to use the numberline to help them.

# Unit 20

How many steps?

1  2  3  4  5  6  7  8  9  10

● Start at 10 go back to 6 _____steps

● Start at 8 go back to 2 _____steps

● Start at 9 go back to 1 _____steps

● Start at 7 go back to 3 _____steps

● Start at 5 go back to 2 _____steps

● Start at 9 go back to 2 _____steps

# Inversion

## In and Out

**You will need:**

A bag or box with 10 cubes or shells in it
Number Cards 1–10 (see the Resource
Guide pages 62–64)

- Ask children to pick up a number card from
  the pile.
  Take that number of cubes out of the bag
  (e.g. 4).
  Say together:
  > There were 10 cubes. I took away 4. How many
  > are left?

  Everyone can then predict how many are left
  in the bag.
  Record 10 − 4 = 6.

  When children are confident start again with a
  full bag of 10 cubes.
  Remove 4 cubes
  Say together:
  > There are now 6 cubes in the bag. I need 10. How
  > many must I put back?

  Record 6 + 4 = 10.

- Repeat this activity with different numbers so
  that children become familiar with counting
  on and back.

## Up and Down

**You will need:**

Interlocking cubes
Number Cards 1–10 (see the Resource
Guide pages 62–64) arranged in a
numberline

- Build a tower of 10 cubes.
  Record on the board, 10 $\longrightarrow$
  Ask a child to choose a number card and show
  it to the class (e.g. 4).
  Take away that number from the tower, (6).

- Record on the board, 10 $\xrightarrow{-4}$ 6 $\longrightarrow$
  Ask children:
  > We started with 10, How many did we take away?
  > How many cubes were left?
  > How did we record this?

  Choose another number to take away. Record
  each stage.

  $$10 \xrightarrow{-4} 6 \xrightarrow{-3} 3 \xrightarrow{-2} 1 \xrightarrow{-1} 0$$

  Carry on until all the cubes have gone,
  recording as you go.

- Ask the children how they can rebuild the
  tower using the recording to help them.
  Encourage them to follow the reverse
  instructions to build the tower.

  $$0 \xrightarrow{+1} 1 \xrightarrow{+2} 3 \xrightarrow{+3} 6 \xrightarrow{+4} 10$$

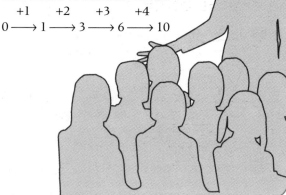

## Mental Workout Unit 21

### Activity Sheet Instructions

Find the missing numbers.

### Teaching Tips for Activity Sheet

Point out the numberline at the bottom of the Activity Sheet.
Before the children start the page show them how to put their
finger on the starting number and count forwards or backwards.
For the less able it may be helpful to provide cards with arrows to
reinforce which way to count on and which way to count back.

Count on $\longrightarrow$   Count back $\longleftarrow$

Start at 3, count on 1

Start at 5, count on 3

Start at 4, count on 5

Start at 4, count back 1

Start at 8, count back 3

Start at 9, count back 5

0   1   2   3   4   5   6   7   8   9   10

# Subtraction sums

## Oral Maths

### Finger Fun

**Working together**

- Practise showing the numbers 0–10 together, using the fingers of one or two hands.
  Ask three children to come out. Ask the first child to put up their fingers to show a number between 0 and 5.
  Then ask the second child to put up their fingers to show a number between 0 and 5.
  Explain that the third child is going to add the numbers of fingers together and show their answer with two hands. Encourage the class to help by counting too. Record the sum.

- Now ask the third child to put down the same amount of fingers as the second child is holding up. If they are right the first child and the third should now be showing the same amount of fingers. Record the sum.

- Choose three more children and repeat the activity.

### Legs

> **You will need:**
>
> A selection of plastic insects and farmyard animals (If possible these should include something with eight legs, six legs, four legs, two legs. If you have any broken animals or insects these will be ideal to create the odd numbers.).

- Ask children to choose two creatures (e.g. cow and ant), then ask:
  *How many legs has the cow? How many legs has the ant?*
  *How many legs have they altogether? How could we show this?*
  Record 4 + 6 = 10.
  Ask children:
  *If the ant crawled away how many legs would be left? How could we record this?*
  Record 10 – 6 = 4.
  Bring the ant back! Ask children:
  *What if the cow had run off? How many legs would be left?*
  *How could we record this?*
  Record: 10 – 4 = 6.

- Repeat this activity to generate lots of addition and subtraction sums.

- To extend this, more able children could choose more than two creatures:
  4 + 8 + 6 = 18, (18 – 4) – 6 =

## *Mental Workout Unit 22*

### Activity Sheet Instructions

Fill in the sums.

### Teaching Tips for Activity Sheet

- Ensure the children understand the first operation before they start the second.

Name _____

_____ + _____ = _____

Now eat two cakes!

_____ − 2 = _____

_____ + _____ = _____

Now eat 3 cakes!

_____ − 3 = _____

# Doubling

## Oral Maths

### Flies

*One fly met one fly on the way to the zoo,*
*The one fly and one fly together made two.*
*Two flies met two flies on the sitting room floor,*
*The two flies and two flies together made four.*
*Three flies met three flies who were up to some tricks,*
*The three flies and three flies together made six.*
*Four flies met four flies – they nearly were late!*
*The four flies and four flies together made eight.*
*Five flies met five flies, creeping out of a den,*
*The five flies and five flies together made ten.*

- Say this rhyme together, using your fingers to represent the groups of flies meeting.
  Touch the fingers together to show there are the same numbers on each hand.
  Put your hands side by side, palms facing the children, to show the total number of flies.

- Extend this to higher numbers

**You will need:**
Cut-out fly shapes
Two hoops

- Place six flies in one hoop. Ask children to put exactly the same number of flies in the other hoop. Count the total number of flies altogether. Start at 6 and count on: 7, 8, 9, 10, 11, 12. Record this 6 + 6 = 12. Say: *double six equals twelve.*

### Twin Towers

**You will need:**
*Multilink* cubes

- Split children into groups and give each group some ready made *Multilink* towers (2, 3, 4, 5 or 6).
  Ask children to make matching twin towers. When each group have made their towers, start working together.
  Have some doubling sums already written on the board:
     1 + 1    2 + 2   3 + 3 etc.
  Take each sum separately. Ask children holding the twin towers that match each sum to come out and help work out the answers.

## *Mental Workout Unit 23*

### Activity Sheet Instructions

Make these into doubling sums.

### Teaching Tips for Activity Sheet

Encourage the children to count the insects in each right-hand hoop and count again as they draw the insects in the left-hand hoop. For children who are having difficulty, the insects can be joined together so that each insect has a partner in the other hoop.

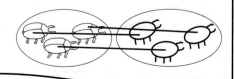

# Unit 23

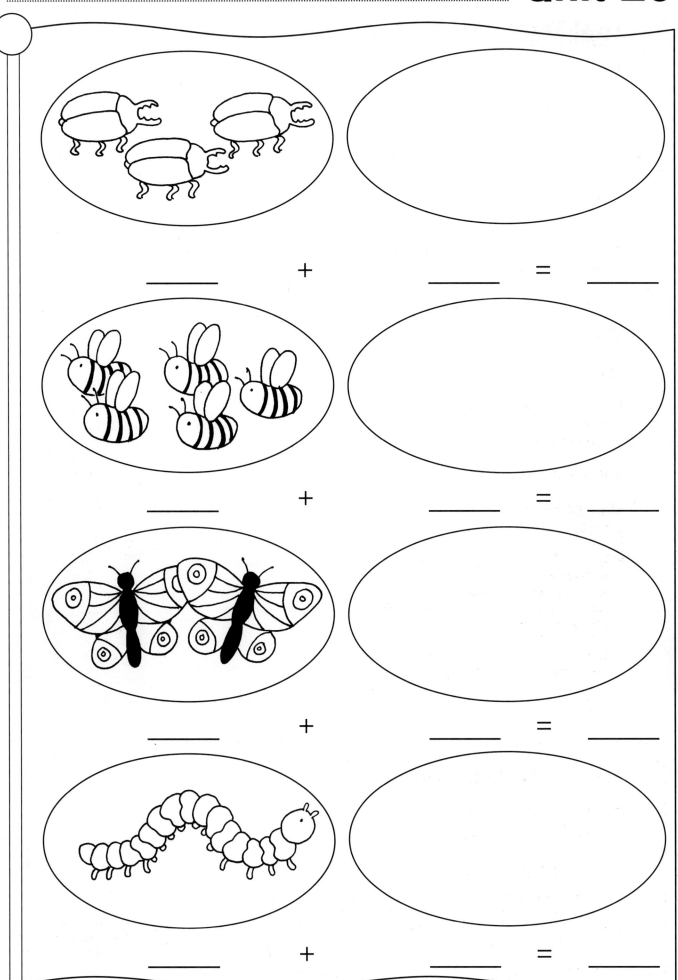

_____  +  _____  =  _____

_____  +  _____  =  _____

_____  +  _____  =  _____

_____  +  _____  =  _____

# Halving

## Oral Maths

### Heads and Tails

- Choose 16 children to stand in a line.
  Count the children together.
  Explain that you are going to ask each child to show either heads or tails.
  For heads the children put their hands on their heads.
  For tails they put their hands on their bottoms so they form birds' tails.
  Go along the line touching each child on the shoulder saying alternately 'heads' or 'tails'.
  Ask the rest of the class:
  *How many children are showing heads?*
  *How many children are showing tails?*
  *Can you think of another way of describing this?*
  Explain that the number of children showing 'heads' is equal to the number showing 'tails'.
  So we can say *half of sixteen is eight.*
  Ask the children showing 'heads' to sit down again.
- Now repeat this activity with eight children.
  This time there will be four showing heads and four showing tails.
  Carry on until you reach half of two equals one.

### Extension

- Repeat the activity starting with larger numbers.
- Bring in different actions so that you sort children into groups of three (thirds) or groups of four (quarters).

### Party Hats

> **You will need:**
> 20 party hats (10 red and 10 blue)

- Hand out the party hats and ask the children to put them on.
  Ask the children with red hats to sit on the right and those with blue hats to sit on the left. Talk to the children about how they can describe what part of the group has red hats and what part of the group has blue.
  Now ask the group with red hats to stand up. Encourage the class to work out how many children there are and what half of that number would be.
  Ask half of the group to sit down.
- Repeat this activity starting with different numbers.
  Continue until you reach an odd number.

## *Mental Workout Unit 24*

### Activity Sheet Instructions

Colour in half the items in each group. The first is done for you.

### Teaching Tips for Activity Sheet

If children have difficulty with the concept of half, share a bar of squared chocolate with them. Talk about how it must be shared fairly.

HAPPY BIRTHDAY

HAPPY BIRTHDAY

# Mixed Addition and Subtraction

## Oral Maths

### Shopping

> **You will need:**
>
> A large Numberline 0–20 (see the Resource Guide pages 62–64)
>
> A selection of small toys, all priced at different amounts under 10p
>
> Five 20p coins
>
> A box of assorted denominations of coins for change

■ Hand out the five 20p coins and invite children to come out and buy two toys.
Work out and record the total price of the two toys, e.g.

| 1 plastic ant | 3p |
|---|---|
| 1 rubber ball | 8p |
| Total cost | 11p |

Then invite children to help work out the change by starting at 11 and counting on to 20 using the Numberline. Encourage children to think up which coins could be given as change.

For example, if change equalled 9p
    1p 1p 1p 1p 1p 1p 1p 1p 1p
    2p 1p 1p 1p 1p 1p 1p 1p
    2p 2p 1p 1p 1p 1p 1p
    2p 2p 2p 1p 1p 1p
    2p 2p 2p 2p 1p
    5p 1p 1p 1p 1p
    5p 2p 1p 1p
    5p 2p 2p

■ Repeat the activity but vary the ways that you calculate the change.
Count back to the total starting at 20.
Count back in twos to amounts that end in even numbers.

### Target Numbers

> **You will need:**
>
> A set of 12 skittles, six red marked 0–5, 6 blue marked 0–5
>
> Bricks marked with '+' and '–' and '=' signs

■ Give each child a target number between 0 and 10.
Ask them how they could make their number if they must use a red and a blue skittle and either a + or a – sign.
Write each sum on the board. The same sum cannot be used more than once to make a target number.

## Mental Workout Unit 25

### Activity Sheet Instructions

Draw the coins you would get as change.

### Teaching Tips for Activity Sheet

■ It may be helpful for children to have access to plastic coins to help with this activity.

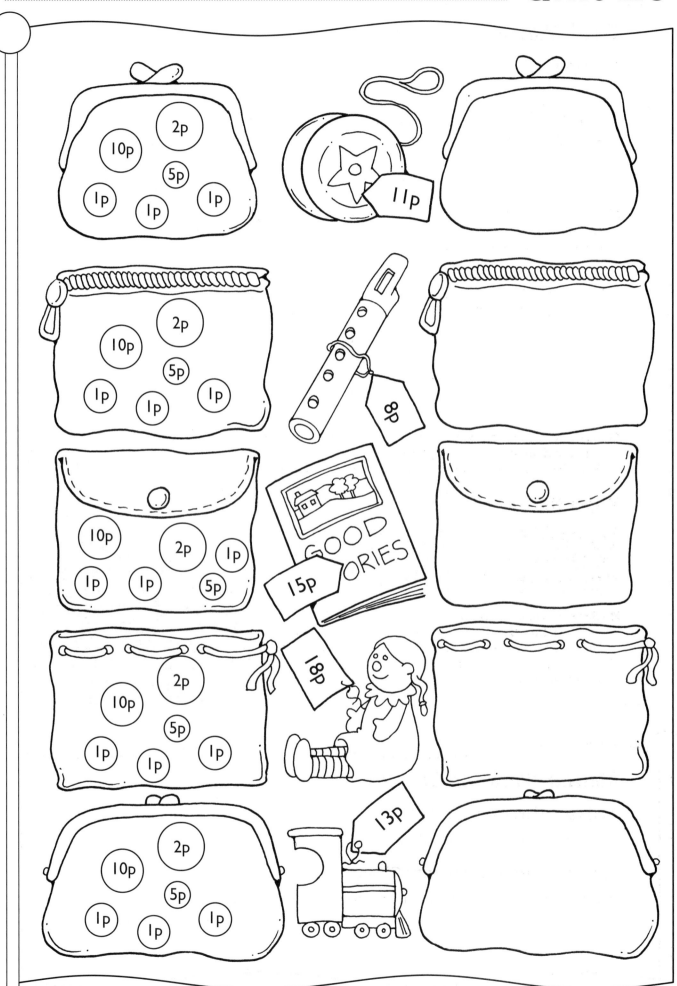

# More Than One Operation

## Oral Maths

### What is the Question?

**You will need:**

16 bricks or counters

- Write on the board the number 16.
  Explain that this is the answer to a sum.
  Show the number frame: __ + __ + __ = 16
  Have your 16 bricks or counters available and ask children to put some of the bricks in each space.
  Record the sum, e.g. 2 + 4 + 10 = 16.
  Ask children: *Could you make a different sum by moving one brick from one space to another?*
      e.g. 3 + 3 + 10 = 16
  *Would there still be 16 bricks altogether?*
  *Could you move two bricks to another space?*
      e.g. 3 + 5 + 8 = 16
  *Would you still have 16 bricks?*

- Choose a different number frame:
  __ + __ + __ + __ = 16
  Share out the bricks again.
      e.g. 1 + 3 + 2 + 10 = 16
  Talk about how you can make new sums that still make 16.

### Playground Friends

**You will need:**

14 model people, e.g. *Lego, Playmobil*

- Explain to the children that these people are a group of playground friends.
  Count together to show that there are 14.
  Divide the people into three unequal groups.
  Record the number of 'friends' in each group.
  Count again to show that there are still 14 in total.
  Record the sum.

- Allow children to rearrange the models into three new groups and repeat the activity.

## *Mental Workout Unit 26*

### Activity Sheet Instructions

Write the sum for each line of ducks.

### Teaching Tips for Activity Sheet

- Encourage the children to say the number first and then count each group of ducks to check whether their guess was right.

# Unit 26

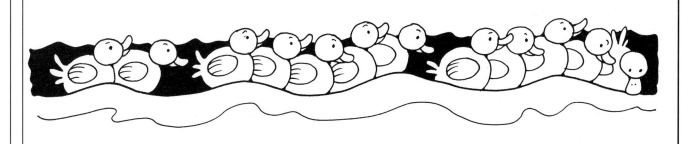

_____ + _____ + _____ = 12

_____ + _____ + _____ = 12

_____ + _____ + _____ = 12

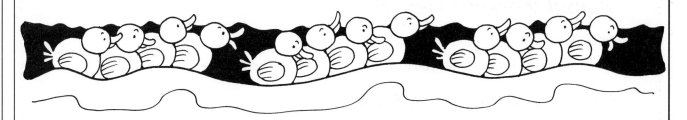

_____ + _____ + _____ = 12

# Odd or Even?

## Oral Maths

### Ladders

- Invite six children to come out to the front.
  Explain that if 6 is an odd number there will be somebody without a partner.
  Ask children to sit facing each other in twos, their legs outstretched, with their feet touching.
  Talk about whether everyone has a partner.

- Now ask a different group of 7 children to come out.
  Again, ask them to sit facing each other in twos with their feet touching. Arrange the pairs to form a ladder.
  There will be one child without a partner.
  Show this child how to step down the 'ladder' of pairs of legs.

- Now ask individual children to come out and choose a number between 1 and 20.
  If they choose an odd number that child can step down the ladder.

### Cups and Saucers

> **You will need:**
> A set of 12 cups and saucers

- Hand out 12 cups and 12 saucers so that they alternate cup, saucer, cup, saucer, around the group.
  Ask children to bring out their cup or saucer one at a time.
  Explain that if there is a cup or saucer left over the number is odd and if the cups and saucers are in pairs the number is even.
  Start with one cup. Explain this is not complete so 1 is an odd number.
  As each child comes out do check that no one has swapped with the child next to them and that the sequence is still cup, saucer, etc. Talk about the cup and the saucer making a pair. Explain that 2 is an even number.
  Carry on round the group until you have made the 12 cups and saucers.

- For reinforcement this activity could be varied by using knives and forks, felt tipped pens with caps, eggs and egg cups, etc.

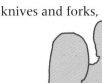

## Mental Workout Unit 27

### Activity Sheet Instructions

Sort these letters for the postmen. Write the correct numbers on their bags.

### Teaching Tips for Activity Sheet

- If classroom pegs are numbered, children with even numbers could get their coats first.
- Before starting the Activity Sheet, explain to the children about the way some streets are numbered, with odd numbers on one side and even on the other.

Name

Mr Shark
1 Rock Avenue
Seatown

MISS STARFISH
3 SAND VIEW
SEATOWN

Master Crab
5 Rockpool Road
Seatown

Mrs Herring
7 Ocean Terrace
Seatown

Dr Whale
9 Sea Bottom
Seatown

MR COD
2 WAVE LANE
SEATOWN

Mr and Mrs Jellyfish
4 Sand View
Seatown

Master Shrimp
6 Rockpool Road
Seatown

MISS PLAICE
8 SEA BOTTOM
SEATOWN

Mr and Mrs Haddock
10 Rock Avenue
Seatown

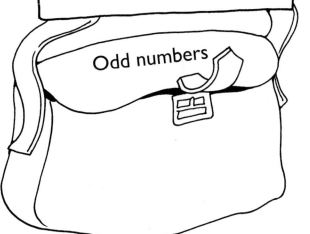

Odd numbers

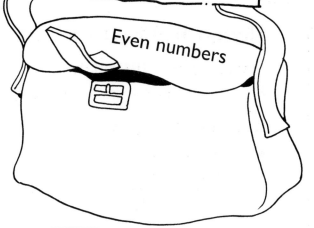

Even numbers

# Balancing Sums

## Oral Maths

### Bucket Balance

- Talk about how you make things balance.
  Demonstrate by putting equal numbers of cubes in
  both buckets. When the children are confident about
  putting the same number of cubes on each side to
  achieve a balance, take the cubes out and write:

**You will need:**
A bucket balance or a bar balance
Interlocking cubes

> 4 cubes    balances    4 cubes

Arrange the groups of cubes into sticks of 3 and 1 and sticks of 2 and 2.
Place them in the buckets, 3 + 1 on one side and 2 + 2 on the other.
Check that they still balance. Write:

> 3 + 1    balances    2 + 2

Ask children to tell you why they think that they still balance.
Continue for different sums that make 6.
For example: 4 + 2 = 3 + 3, 4 + 2 = 5 + 1, 3 + 3 = 6 + 0.

- Repeat using a different total.

### See-saw

**You will need:**
An up-turned bucket or bowl
A skipping rope

- Make a pretend see-saw on the floor of the classroom, using the rope to represent the
  plank of the see-saw, and the upturned bucket or bowl to represent its middle.
  Ask two children to sit at one end of the see-saw. Now add two more at the same end.
  Record the sum: 2 + 2 = 4.
  Now ask another child to sit at the other end of the see-saw.
  Ask: *How many more children do we need to join him/her?*
  Record 1 + 3 = 4.
  The see-saw now balances!
- Repeat using different numbers of children up to the
  capacity of the 'plank'!

## *Mental Workout Unit 28*

### Activity Sheet Instructions

Write sums to make the buckets balance.

### Teaching Tips for Activity Sheet

- Explain to the children that the sums must total the same answer, for the buckets to balance.

# Unit 28

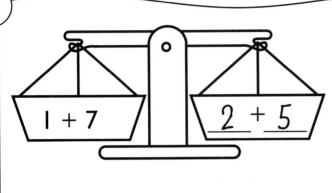

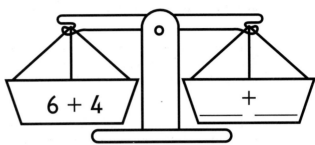

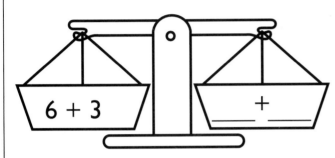

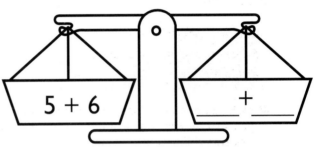

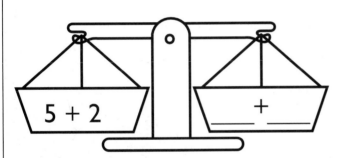

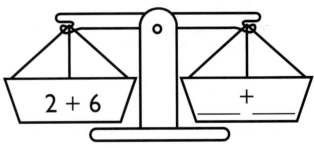

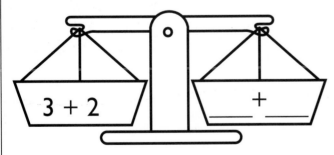

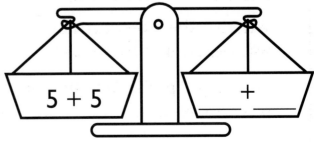

# Fun time

# Unit 29

## Aliens

■ Make cards in the shape of various spaceships and write on each card the sort of alien that is hiding in this ship, e.g. 2 heads, 4 legs, 6 ears.
Hand out cards for children to draw aliens.

## Circle Counting

**You will need:**
A bean bag

■ The aim is to throw the bean bag around the group and as each person catches it they say the next number: 1, 2, 3, etc.
■ You can play this with smaller groups and if someone misses a turn another child takes their place.
■ Extend the activity by counting in twos or tens.

## Things I Can Do in a Minute

**You will need:**
Dice
Interlocking cubes
String and beads
Dried peas and a straw
Clock or watch

■ How many times can you write a number 2?
■ How many times can you throw a 6 with a dice?
■ How tall can you build a tower using interlocking cubes?
■ How long can you make a snake threading beads?
■ How many peas can you pick up (by sucking through a straw) and put in a beaker?
■ Ask children to estimate a number for each activity. Then when they complete each activity they can compare the results.

## Number Hop!

**You will need:**
Several PE hoops
Number Cards 1–20 (see the Resource Guide pages 62–64)
A large space!

■ Spread the PE hoops around the floor. Place a number card in each hoop.
Play a game which is similar to musical chairs, but when the music stops children must stand in a hoop with an even number, a number greater than 3, a number less than 10, an odd number etc. Encourage the first child in each hoop to pick up the number card and hold it up high to prevent damage!

# Mental Maths record sheet

| | Oral Maths | | Learning Objective | |
|---|---|---|---|---|
| 1 | Counting skills | | To develop early counting skills | |
| 2 | Numbers 1–5 | | To become familiar with the numerals that represent numbers 1–5 | |
| 3 | Sequences | | To memorise sequences of numbers | |
| 4 | 1–10 numberline | | To introduce the 1–10 numberline | |
| 5 | Finger counting | | To introduce finger counting | |
| 6 | Ordering 1–10 | | To practise ordering numbers 1–10 | |
| 7 | Numbers 11–20 | | To become familiar with numbers 11–20 | |
| 8 | Numbers to 100 | | To introduce larger numbers to 100 | |
| 9 | Twos and tens | | To practise counting in twos and tens | |
| 10 | Ordering 1–20 | | To practise ordering numbers 0–20 | |
| 11 | More or less | | To use mathematical language such as more or less with numbers 0–20 | |
| 12 | Estimating | | To develop estimation skills | |
| 13 | What comes next? | | To practise ordering of non-sequential numbers | |
| 14 | Making five | | To practise ways of making 5 | |
| 15 | Simple addition | | To practise adding 2 single digit numbers | |
| 16 | Counting on | | To practise the skill of counting on addition | |
| 17 | Number Bonds | | To practise number bonds to 10 | |
| 18 | Solving problems | | To introduce using addition to solve problems | |
| 19 | Partioning | | To introduce partitioning sets as a beginning to subtraction | |
| 20 | Counting back 10–0 | | To practise counting back from 10–0 | |
| 21 | Inversion | | To introduce the inverse nature of addition and subtraction | |
| 22 | Subtraction sums | | To use known addition to create subtraction sums | |
| 23 | Doubling | | To practise doubling numbers to 10 | |
| 24 | Halving | | To introduce halves linked to the concept of number | |
| 25 | Mixed Addition and Subtraction | | To introduce mixed addition and subtraction using money | |
| 26 | More than one operation | | To introduce the idea that there are lots of ways of making any number | |
| 27 | Odd or Even | | To introduce odd and even numbers | |
| 28 | Balancing sums | | To introduce the idea that different number operations can make the same number | |
| 29 | Fun time | | To practise numbers using numbers 0–20 | |

# RESOURCE GUIDE

*This is a guide to some of the resources referred to in the ORAL maths activities in this book. You can either make these resources, following the descriptions and illustrations, or they can be ordered from NES Arnold, Ludlow Hill Road, West Bridgford, Nottingham, NG2 6HD, when a catalogue number is supplied at the end of the resource reference.*

## Number Cards

Twenty cards bearing the numbers from one to twenty. These can be copied from the illustration below or ordered from NES Arnold in three sizes (Cat. No. NB9631/5 Standard, NB9734/3 Large and NB9739/8 Teacher's).

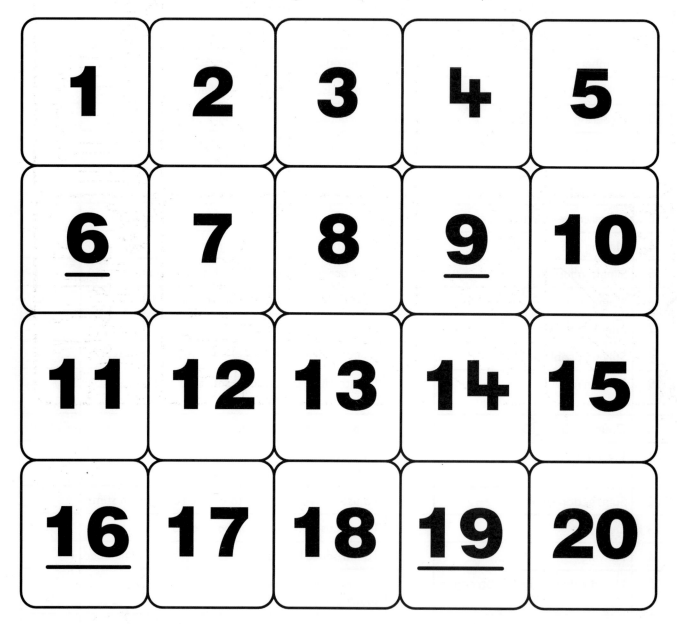

## Mathematical Washing Line

A length of string and at least twenty-one pegs strung between two walls. These can be home-made or ordered from NES Arnold (Cat. No. NB7717/2) as a Mathematical Washing Line set, including: three sets of cards (Numeral set 0–20, Quantity set 0–20 and Number word 0–20); Washing line; Pegs and Snap fasteners for easy anchorage.

## Numberline

A large wall mounted strip of card bearing the numbers from zero to twenty in a line. This can be home-made or ordered from NES Arnold (Cat. No. NB8509/6) as a Numberlines – Wall set, including: PVC numberlines marked 0–100, 0–20, 0–10 and -10–10.

## Picture cards of dogs and bones

Ten cards bearing a picture of a dog with one, two, three, four, five, six, seven, eight, nine or ten bones. These can be copied from the illustration below.

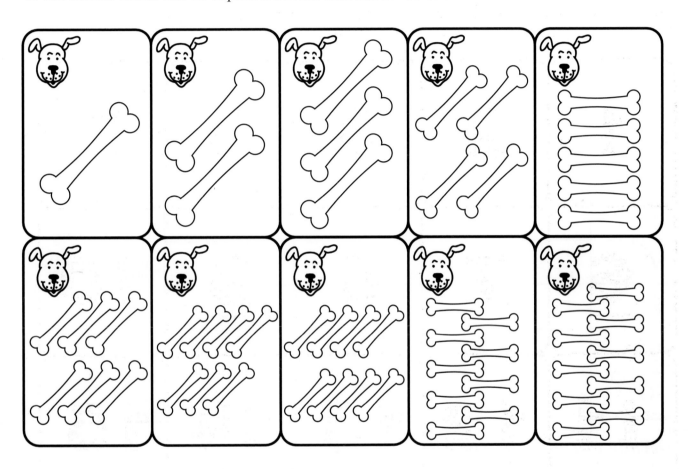

## Addition Square

A square twelve-by-twelve grid with a plus sign in the top left-hand square and the numbers from one to ten running along the top and down the left-hand side squares. This can be copied from the illustration below.

| + | 0 | 1 | 2 | 3 | 4 | 5 | 6 | 7 | 8 | 9 | 10 |
|---|---|---|---|---|---|---|---|---|---|---|----|
| 0 | | | | | | | | | | | |
| 1 | | | | | | | | | | | |
| 2 | | | | | | | | | | | |
| 3 | | | | | | | | | | | |
| 4 | | | | | | | | | | | |
| 5 | | | | | | | | | | | |
| 6 | | | | | | | | | | | |
| 7 | | | | | | | | | | | |
| 8 | | | | | | | | | | | |
| 9 | | | | | | | | | | | |
| 10 | | | | | | | | | | | |

## Decade Cards

Ten cards bearing the decades from ten to one hundred. These can be copied from the illustration below or ordered from NES Arnold in three sizes (Cat. No. NB9632/8 Standard, NB9737/2 Large and NB9735/6 Teacher's).

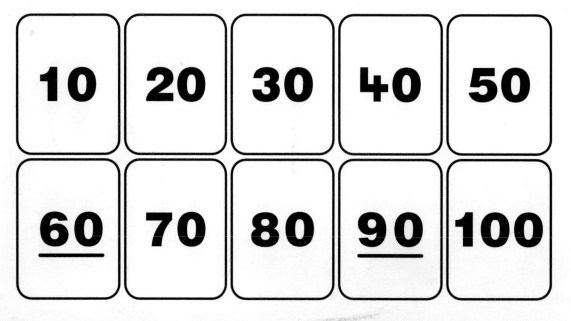